HI READERS, HERE I COME... YEEEEE!!!

STORIES

SEE AND SMILE

IT HAPPENED TO ME

THE GREAT OUTDOORS

ANIMALS AND YOU

HE IS GOING TO CRASH INTO ME ... AS USUAL!!!

MEET SHIKARI SHAMBU

Left to himself, Shikari Shambu would sleep the whole day long…

His dreams are seldom completed because….

… Shanti, his wife and manager hates to see him wasting his time!

BUT WHERE THERE'S A WILL THERE'S A WAY! AND WITH HIS INCREDIBLE LUCK, SHIKARI SHAMBU ALWAYS COMES OUT ON TOP!

Elephant Rides. Only Rs 10

4

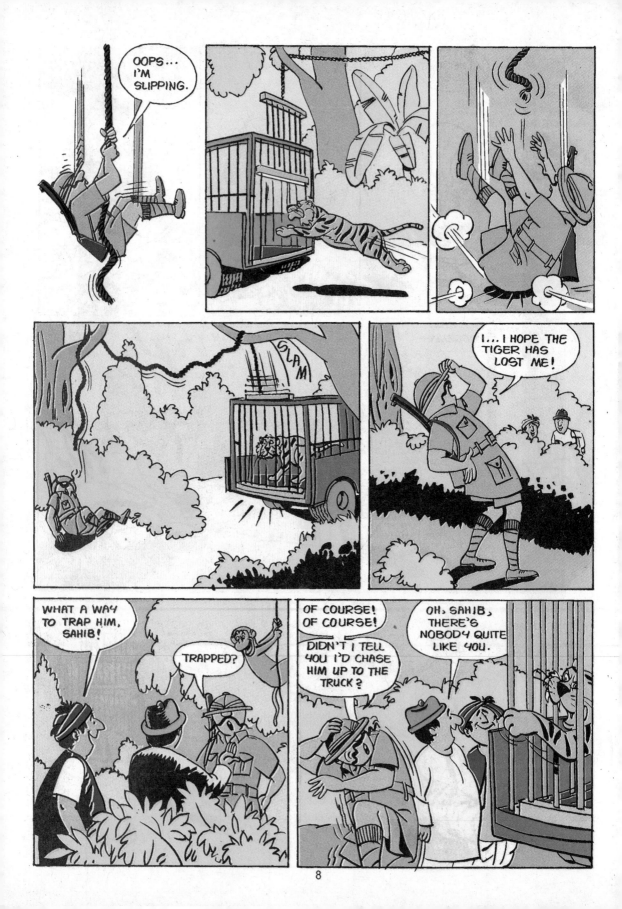

See and Smile

Raghu

I WANT AN EGG.

I'M SORRY...

WE SELL EGGS ONLY BY THE DOZEN.

WELL THEN GIVE ME ½TH OF A DOZEN.

This happened to me

A sparrow had built a nest in the top corner of a wall cupboard. The chicks used to scream throughout the day for food. The sparrow would hunt for worms and feed them. One evening when we were packing our clothes to go on a holiday, the sparrow flew into our house through the ventilator and hit the rotating fan. She fell down and died on the spot.

Her chicks screamed throughout the night for food. My father and I were wondering what would happen to the chicks after we left in a few days. So we decided to keep the ventilator open and prayed to God for the safety of the chicks. Wonder of wonders, early the next morning we found another mother-sparrow feeding the hungry chicks!

This true-life story was sent by Sharada R. Iyer of Mumbai

10

13

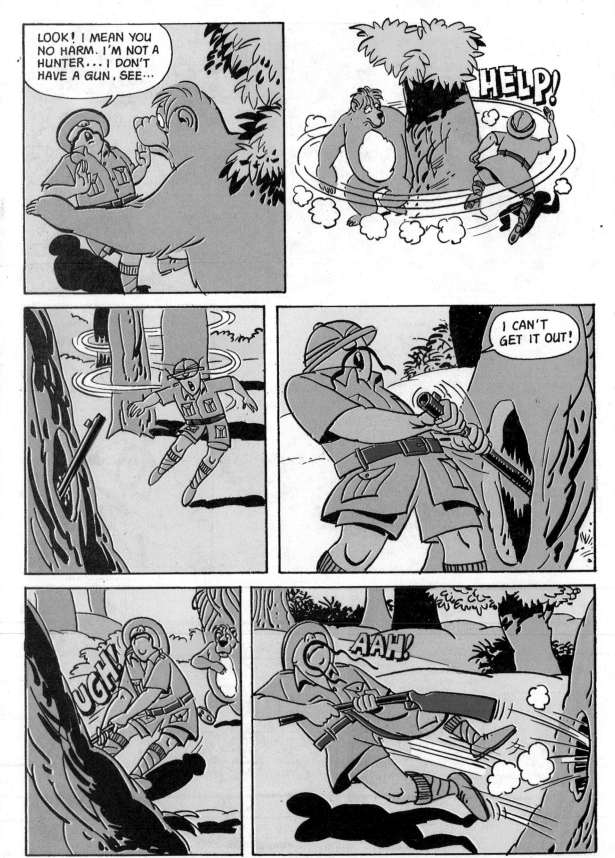

16

Animals & you

TAIL TALK WITH MANEKA GANDHI

There is a common belief that cats love a house and its surroundings more than the human who cares for it and feeds it. This is not true.

Cats are certainly more comfortable in a known territory and will take time adjusting to a new one. But once you have made a pet of a cat you cannot leave her behind when you move out of that house. The animal gets accustomed to food at regular times and loses the skill to find it for herself. If that food and water becomes unavailable she will starve, become ill and even die.

When a cat is adopted she presumes that she is a member of that family. When she rubs herself against you, she is exchanging smells, which she does only with someone whom she trusts. She depends on you for shelter and affection.

When we adopt a dog or a cat or any animal we must remember that he becomes our responsibility for the whole of his life. When we move house we never forget to take our clothes and toys. How can we abandon a living creature that depends on us?

Clever Creature

The octopus blocks the entrance to its den with a door made of rocks.

Quote

If animals were made by God for man's use, how come they were on earth long centuries before man was made! - Adapted from Henry Salt

IT HAPPENED TO ME

LOOKING FOR THE PEARLS

This happened to me when my aunt visited us along with her one-and-a-half-year-old child and the child's nurse, Shusee. From the moment Shusee arrived she sat engrossed in front of the TV and did not utter a word. Suddenly when she spoke, my mother laughed and told her that she was dropping pearls from her mouth. Not realizing that it had been said figuratively she jumped from her seat and began looking for the pearls.

> Based on a true-life incident sent by: R.K. Sri Nivedita, New Scheme Road, M.L. Puram, Pollachi – 642 002.

CLOSE SHAVE

Once during my exams I woke up at about two in the morning to revise my lessons. I took my books to the TV room so as not to disturb anybody. I finished revising by three and decided to go back to bed. As I crept back to my bedroom in the dark I stumbled across a chair and that made quite a noise. My parent's bedroom was near the TV room and my father heard the noise. He grabbed a steel rod and struck the floor, hoping to scare away what he thought was a thief. I quickly got into bed and pulled up the covers.

In the morning my father told us what had happened the night before. I told him it was only me stumbling upon a chair. Everybody started laughing. I still remember that steel rod that was almost used to thrash me.

> Based on a true-life incident sent by: Jason W. Manners, c/o R. Langsteih, Nongrah (Nongpdeng), P.O. Umpling, Shillong -793 006, Meghalaya.

21

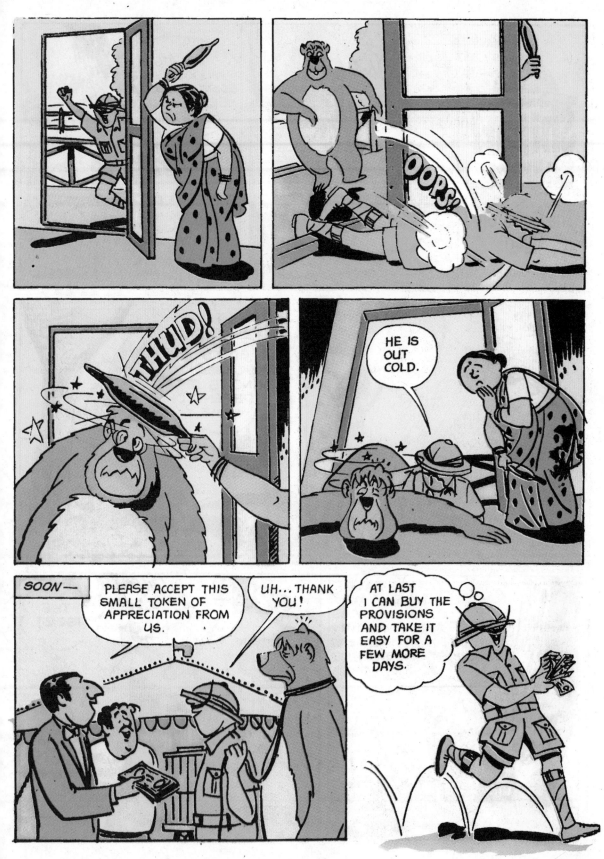

See and Smile

IT HAPPENED TO ME....

One day, my father gave me a rupee and asked me to get some blades. On the way to the shop, I found a rupee coin on the road. I was very happy. I went to a shop and bought sweets. Then I went to buy the blades. When I put my hand into my pocket I found there was no money. Then I realised that the coin I had found had fallen from my own pocket, pushed out when I had put my hand into it to take out some marbles. Needless to say I got a severe scolding from my father when I went home without the blades.

A true-life incident sent by
Master S. Karthik, 856,
4th main Road, Vijayanagar,
Bangalore-560 040

Once we had a cat named Tiger. We loved it very much. But it grew very naughty and once it even stole the fish from the kitchen. From that day on, we stopped it from entering the house. One day while we were sitting in the drawing room, we heard a soft knock on the door and ran to answer it. We were amazed to see the cat walk in. Later we found that the cat had learnt to jump up and give the door a soft knock.

A true-life
incident sent by
Aparna Raut Desai,
Rua-de-Ourem,
Neugi Nagar, Panaji,
Goa-403001

Goutam.

ARE WE BIDDING FAREWELL TO THE RHINOCEROS?

Script: Luis Fernandes

Illustrations: Gautam Sen

A SHOT RINGS OUT IN THE NIGHT. THE RHINOCEROS STUMBLES AND FALLS. THE HORN ON ITS HEAD HAS COST IT ITS LIFE.

IN ASIA THERE IS A WIDESPREAD BELIEF THAT RHINOCEROS HORN CAN CURE A NUMBER OF DISEASES. DOCTORS HAVE FOUND THAT THESE SO-CALLED MEDICINES ARE USELESS BUT PEOPLE CONTINUE TO HAVE FAITH IN THEM...

RHINOCERUS & ANTELOPE HORN FEBRIFUGAL TABLETS

RHINO-HORN CHIPS.

IN NEPAL, MYANMAR, CHINA AND THAILAND EVEN THE FLESH AND BLOOD OF THE ANIMAL IS CONSIDERED TO HAVE CURATIVE POWERS.

IN YEMEN, POSSESSING A DAGGER WITH A RHINO-HORN HANDLE IS A SIGN OF MANHOOD AND WEALTH. COUNTLESS RHINOS HAVE DIED AND CONTINUE TO DIE FOR YEMENI VANITY.

DAGGERS WITH RHINO-HORN HANDLE FOR SALE IN NORTH YEMEN.

AFRICA HAS TWO SPECIES OF RHINOCEROS. THE BLACK RHINOCEROS AND THE WHITE RHINOCEROS. LESS THAN A CENTURY AGO, THERE WERE HUNDREDS OF THOUSANDS OF RHINOS IN AFRICA. NOW ONLY ABOUT 13,000 REMAIN.

THE BLACK RHINOCEROS

THE WHITE RHINOCEROS HAS BROAD SQUARE LIPS.

THERE ARE THREE SPECIES OF RHINOCEROS IN ASIA: THE INDIAN, THE JAVAN AND THE SUMATRAN RHINOCEROS.

SUMATRAN RHINO

JAVA RHINO

GREAT INDIAN RHINOCEROS

ASIAN RHINOCEROSES, LIKE THEIR AFRICAN COUSINS HAVE BEEN UNDER THE GUN FOR CENTURIES. IN THE DAYS WHEN THE SWORD WAS THE CHIEF WEAPON, SHIELDS MADE OF RHINOCEROS HIDE WERE IN GREAT DEMAND AND THE ANIMALS WERE SLAUGHTERED BY THE THOUSANDS IN OUR COUNTRY.

THE LATEST TALLY

THE JAVA SPECIES IS DWINDLING. THERE ARE NOT EVEN A HUNDRED ANIMALS LEFT.

THE SUMATRAN RHINOCEROSES NUMBER ABOUT 300.

THE INDIAN RHINO NUMBERS LESS THAN 2500. THEY ARE RESTRICTED ALMOST ENTIRELY TO EIGHT SMALL PROTECTED AREAS IN ASSAM, WEST BENGAL AND NEPAL. THE FUTURE LOOKS BLEAK FOR THE WORLD'S SECOND-HEAVIEST LAND ANIMAL.

POSTER DESIGNED BY A WILDLIFE PROTECTION GROUP

STOP KILLING RHINOS

A DESPERATE MEASURE

IN NAMIBIA, AFRICA, FOREST RANGERS ARE TRYING OUT AN UNIQUE EXPERIMENT. THEY ARE CUTTING OFF THE HORNS OF THE ANIMALS TO MAKE THE ANIMALS UNATTRACTIVE TO POACHERS.

REMOVING THE HORN (WHICH IS MADE OF KERATIN, THE SAME SUBSTANCE AS OUR FINGERNAILS) DEPRIVES THE AFRICAN RHINO OF A WEAPON OF ATTACK BUT DOES NOT CAUSE IT ANY PHYSICAL DISTRESS.

PERHAPS THE SAME MEASURE COULD BE TRIED OUT IN OUR COUNTRY. THE INDIAN RHINO DOES NOT USE ITS HORN EVEN WHILE FIGHTING.

THE RHINOCEROS IS FIRST PUT TO SLEEP BY SHOOTING A 'FLYING SYRINGE' CONTAINING A DRUG INTO ITS BODY. THEN THE HORN IS SAWED OFF.

See and Smile

Dear Shambu
Our hearts beat about 72 times a minute. How much faster does an elephant's heart beat?
Ada Tayde, *23 Yusuf Manzil Kandivli, Mumbai*

Dear Ada,

Generally, the smaller the animal, the faster its heartbeat. The hummingbird's heart beats at the rate of about 1000 times a minute; the adult human heart, as you have noted, beats at the rate of about 72 beats a minute (though mine, I suspect, goes up to 1000 times a minute in times of danger). The elephant is a big animal. Its heart beats about 25 times a minute.

Dear Shambu
Is there any bird that could defeat a man in a fight?
Mukesh Sood, *A-603, Sector 19 Noida, U.P.*

Dear Mukesh,
There's one bird I would not like to run into, and that is the cassowary. Fortunately it's not found in our country, being a native of Australia and New Guinea. The cassowary is a tall bird, like an ostrich but its legs are more powerful than an ostrich's, and it has knifelike claws. A kick from a cassowary can cripple or even kill a man.

Dear Shambu
Can you tell me which is the world's hardiest tree?
Pooja Sharma, *Gera Enclave, Viman Nagar, Pune*

Dear Pooja,

Some trees can live hundreds of years but in terms of hardiness I think the prize would surely go to the Ombu tree of Argentina. This tree is almost impossible to destroy.

Its wood is so moist that you can't burn down the tree, and the trunk is so spongy that an axe bounces off it. It can survive insect attacks and the most intense heat. It can get by on very little water. Sometimes in violent storms, it is the only tree left standing for miles around.

Dear Shambu
I read somewhere that a crocodile can outrun a horse. Is it true?
Shruti Desai, *Sarangpani Street, T.Nagar Chennai - 600 017*

Dear Shruti,

Crocodiles can run surprisingly fast on land, but only for a short period. They start huffing and puffing after about 20 or 30 metres so I doubt very much if a crocodile would be able to outrun a horse, even over a short distance. I think even a man, if he's fit and healthy, would be able to outrun a croc. But don't ever attempt a race with that reptile. It might be more fit and healthier than you!

Dear Shambu
Butterflies are such gentle creatures. Do they ever fight among themselves?
Erica Rodrigues, *29, Rai, Moira, Goa*

Dear Erica,

Male butterflies of some species are known to fight over territory. They rush out to intercept intruders. They flash their colours and flutter their wings aggressively and may even make physical contact but I don't think they can hurt each other too much.

39

40

42

44

THE HOOLOCK GIBBON

Script: Luis Fernandes
Illustrations: Ajit Vasaikar

THERE IS A HOWLING IN A FOREST IN ASSAM. SOUNDS OF "HOO-HOO" FILL THE AIR.

THEN YOU SEE THEM — SHORT, LONG-ARMED APES SWINGING EFFORTLESSLY THROUGH THE TREETOPS IN FAMILY GROUPS OF 4 TO 6 MEMBERS EACH.
THEY ARE HOOLOCK GIBBONS, THE ONLY APES FOUND IN INDIA.

EACH GROUP SETTLES ON THE TREES WHICH MARK THE BOUNDARY OF THE TERRITORY IT CONSIDERS ITS OWN.

ONE LARGE MALE, WATCHED ANXIOUSLY BY HIS MATE AND THEIR OFFSPRING (ONE OF WHOM IS HOLDING ON TIGHTLY TO HIS MOTHER) SWAGGERS OUT OF THE LIMITS OF HIS OWN TERRITORY.

... AND IS IMMEDIATELY CHALLENGED BY HIS ANGRY NEIGHBOUR.

CLAWS AND TEETH FLASH IN THE MORNING SUN...

... AND THE INTRUDER RUNS AWAY.

THERE IS MORE HOWLING AND THEN THE GROUPS DISPERSE.

THIS YOUNG MALE CONSIDERS HIMSELF TOO OLD TO STAY WITH HIS FAMILY. SO HE LIVES ON THE BORDERS OF THE FAMILY TERRITORY.

HE, LIKE ALL OTHER GIBBONS, LIVES MAINLY ON FRUITS LIKE FIGS, MANGOES AND GRAPES. BUT HE ALSO EATS LEAVES, INSECTS, EGGS AND SOMETIMES BIRDS.

HE LEAPS FROM TREE TO TREE IN SEARCH OF FOOD. SOME OF THE TREES ARE MORE THAN 7 M APART.

SWINGING THROUGH THE TREETOPS HOWEVER, HAS ITS HAZARDS. A ROTTEN BRANCH BREAKS OFF IN THE HANDS OF OUR FRIEND...

...AND IT IS ONLY HIS LONG REACH AND HIS AGILITY WHICH SAVES HIM.

GIBBONS ARE THE MOST AGILE MAMMALS IN THE WORLD. THEY HAVE EVEN BEEN SEEN CATCHING BIRDS IN MID-AIR.

LOWERING HIMSELF TO THE GROUND THE GIBBON SHAMBLES TOWARDS ANOTHER TREE. GIBBONS ARE THE ONLY APES WHO HABITUALLY WALK UPRIGHT.

THE OTHER APES CAN WALK UPRIGHT TOO BUT THEY PREFER TO WALK ON ALL FOURS.

CHIMPANZEE

GORILLA

ONE DAY IN JUNE WHICH IS THEIR MATING SEASON, HE FINDS HIS LIFE-PARTNER.

SHE, LIKE HIM, HAS LEFT HER FAMILY BECAUSE SHE HAS BECOME AN ADULT.

THE MALE WILL NOW ESTABLISH HIS OWN TERRITORY ON WHICH HE AND HIS MATE WILL FEED AND LIVE...

... AND REAR OFFSPRING.

THE HOOLOCK GIBBON BECAUSE OF DWINDLING FORESTS IS TODAY AN ENDANGERED SPECIES. SPREAD OVER THE REST OF ASIA HOWEVER, ARE FIVE OTHER SPECIES OF GIBBON THAT ARE NUMEROUS IN THE WILD.

SIAMANG GIBBON

ONE SPECIES, THE SIAMANG GIBBON HAS A LARGE THROAT BAG WHICH IT USES WHEN CALLING. AS IT BREATHES IN, THE BAG FILLS WITH AIR AND A LOUD BOOM IS PRODUCED.

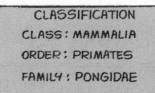

CLASSIFICATION

CLASS : MAMMALIA

ORDER : PRIMATES

FAMILY : PONGIDAE

52

55

60

A few years ago, we enacted a play based on the story of William Tell for our school's annual day function. I was given the role of Tell. The rehearsals progressed swiftly but we had a problem with the scene in which William Tell shoots an arrow and pierces the apple kept on his son's head.

We solved it by using an almost invisible thread, one end of which ran through an already cut apple, and the other through the hollow shaft of the arrow.

The idea worked well at the rehearsals. But on the big day it was a flop. I released the arrow without fully drawing back the bowstring.

The result was that the arrow went only half-way along the thread and stopped in the middle.

I felt so embarassed that I ran out from the stage, throwing away my bow and arrows, to the accompaniment of loud laughter from the audience.

A true-life incident sent by
Waseem Jamadar,
1st Citadelle, L.B.S. Marg, Kurla, Mumbai 400 070

One day when I was going to school by bus, I saw the conductor scolding a passenger because he couldn't pay for his ticket. He stopped the bus and asked the passenger to get out. I laughed loudly at the man's plight.

Just then, a man in his forties sitting beside me got up and bought the poor passenger his ticket. As the bus drove on he rebuked me for laughing, but I did not heed his words.

Soon I was in my class and it was the English period. Our new teacher walked in. I stared in horror for it was the same man who had sat beside me in the bus, and bought the poor man his ticket. When he came in he looked at me and gave me a broad smile. I heaved a sigh of relief. After this incident, I resolved that I would never laugh at the misfortune of others.

A true-life incident sent by Rajesh Iyer, Dombivili (W), Thane District

64

65

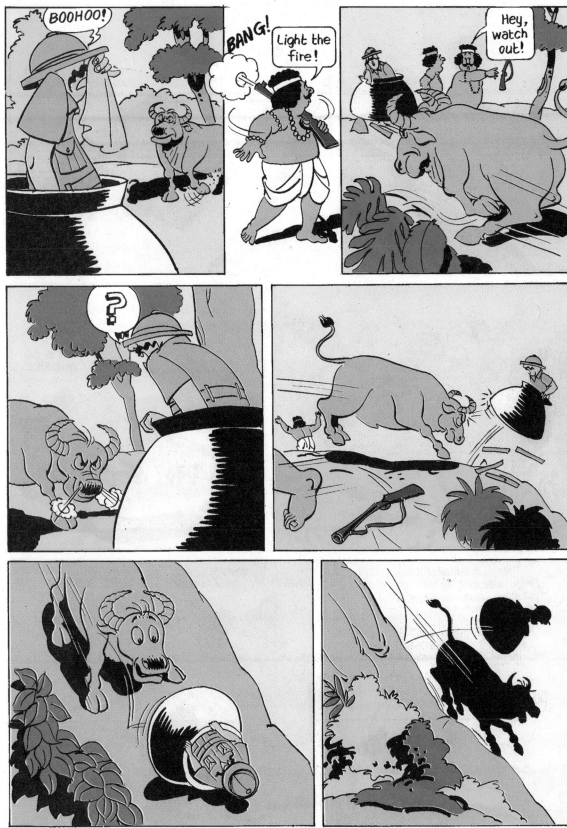

70